No Dream Is Too Big!
KALAKALA COMES HOME

By Judith A. Ennes

Illustrations by Kathy Wilburn • Book Design by Deane Ingram

To Kevin —
Dream your dreams
and believe!
Judith Ennes
11·2·2000

No Dream Is Too Big
KALAKALA COMES HOME

ISBN: 0-9660092-7-4
LCC: 00-100734

For information about permission to reproduce
selections from this book, write to:
Puget Sound Press
6523 California Ave. SW
PMB292
Seattle, WA 98136-1833
http://www.pugetsoundpress.com
psp@pugetsoundpress.com

Book Design Dean Ingram
Illustrations Kathy Wilburn

1 2 3 4 5 6 7 8 9 0

This book is dedicated to Peter Bevis and his helpers, who remembered or recognized the Kalakala's magic. Their determination to rescue and return the Kalakala to Seattle is truly an inspirational lesson of perseverance.

A special thanks to my husband, John, and to Patricia and Lorenzo Leonard, my publishers. Their encouragement and belief in the magic of the Kalakala was invaluable during the busy but invigorating time of publication. Also, I'd like to thank George Bigley, the Kalakala Foundation Archivist, for assisting in our search for historical photos.

A percentage of the proceeds from the sale of this book is donated to the Kalakala Foundation.

Kalakala Foundation
154 N 35th St.
Seattle, WA 98103
(206) 632-0540
http://www.kalakala.org

Artist's dedication: To Ian with love - Kathy Wilburn

Forward

I first saw the KALAKALA from the deck of the halibut schooner PIONEER as we headed out of Kodiak Harbor on my first trip as an Alaskan fisherman.

Standing on the deck of the old wood schooner, feeling the gathering swell, endlessly baiting the 15,000 hooks, my eye caught a strange and wondrous sight! There, in the back of a beautiful cove, hidden behind the chaos of the shacks and structures of a cannery's corrugated tin, behind the booms of cranes and the bobbing masts of a few fishing boats, were sweeping graceful curves, lined with big round portholes.

I asked the crewman next to me, "What in the world is that?" "Oh that's some old ferry boat from Seattle." He growled. "Keep baiting". 'Huh', I thought. 'I live in Seattle.' This was in 1984.

I had decided to make Seattle my home five years earlier, and was building my concrete sculpture studio. I found my self broke, in debt and getting a divorce. I sought the refuge of the sea, and the opportunity to earn enough money to continue building my sculpture studio, a place to cast bronze.

Well, we fished those four days. and worked around the clock. We each took a turn for a 3 hour nap, sleeping in our bunks, in our rain gear because the deck above leaked. We ate three meals in those four days and sweated in our slickers wrestling with fish that were sometimes bigger than I was. Rain slashed our faces, and the North Pacific washed the decks. The baiting of hooks became a surreal existence. The counting of time was useless. We filled the hold, and delivered a deck-load as well, 65,000 lbs. of protein. I learned a new dimension of how hard humans can work with out food or sleep.

This knowledge of human capacity would serve us well when the crews eventually got to work on the rescue of the KALAKALA.

As tired and spent as we all were, I found myself still awake, still running on adrenaline, standing on the port side of the PIONEER, as we returned to Kodiak to deliver the ocean's bounty. I was hoping for another glimpse at those strange and wondrous curves lined with big portholes. Someone told me the name of the ship back in there was the KALAKALA.

For four years, I would travel north and fish again to earn cash to continue building my studio. In Seattle, I began to learn more about the KALAKALA. I'd see photos, murals, and asked questions. I gradually began to realize just how important the KALAKALA was to this young city of Seattle. She was the ICON of this city. She made news around the world when she was launched in 1935. I began to believe that the KALAKALA was the thing that put Seattle on the map of the international cities of the world. She was as significant as the Eiffel Tower is to Paris, or the Empire State building is to New York. More importantly, to the sculptor in me, she represented our imagination, our creativity, and the boldness of our pioneering spirit to go ahead and build something that had never been done before.

Against all odds, the KALAKALA was created in the uncertainty of the Great Depression, expressly as a way to help people to feel good, to feel the hope and promise of a shining future. The KALAKALA was the symbol of our community, and for the many that she served, she was a gathering place, our community center.

After each fishing season, year after year, I learned more about what the KALAKALA represented. I began to feel dismayed about the way our new American culture has a tendency to simply consume and discard, oftentimes without giving a second thought as to the value of what is being discarded . And here sat the remarkable KALAKALA, abandoned and discarded in a remote cove in Kodiak, Alaska.

In 1988, I resolved to spend some time on land, to see a little bit more of Alaska than what I had seen through a pair of binoculars from the pitching deck of a halibut long-line boat. The first thing I did was to find my way to that remote cove, to get a closer look at those strange and wondrous curves.

I met Mr. Gill Reel, the caretaker of the KALAKALA, and he said "Sure you can look through the boat, oh, here's a flashlight, don't fall in any holes!"

I went from bottom to top, prop shaft to bow anchors, and every room in between. As I finally stood on top, seeing her streamlined smokestack, I said out loud "Too cool of a boat to lose! The KALAKALA is coming home'!" I resolved then and there that I would do what I could to return the KALAKALA to her rightful place as the Queen of Puget Sound.

That very morning, in October of 1988, I began negotiating with the City of Kodiak, the owners of the boat. I returned to Seattle and shared the news, the excitement; the dream was born. In 1989, the EXXON VALDEZ spilled it's cargo of oil and no one in Kodiak wanted to talk about the KALAKALA. For the first seven years, it seemed that I'd take a step or two forward and get knocked back just as soon. I finally decided that sometimes the tide is in, and sometimes the tide is out. I bided my time. The KALAKALA continued to rust and deteriorate.

In August of 1995, I had two file drawers of papers on the KALAKALA. And still she rusted and deteriorated. I re-examined my approach and asked, 'what would a sculptor do?' We sculptors work direct! We work with our hands! I resolved; "No more meetings, no more notes, let's get to work on the boat! Let's work direct!

So we got to work. Friends and fellow sculptors came north. A tiny administration staff was assembled in Seattle. Our greatest resource was the diverse skills and creative solutions the crew brought with them. We lived and worked on fresh air and a prayer, but we kept at it.

The winters would freeze our food and water. Most everyone said the task was too enormous. Ten thousand voices told us that it could never be done. Sometimes there was only one crewman on the job in Kodiak. But the KALAKALA had magic, and everything that we needed seemed to be literally an arms reach away.

I cannot speak enough of the unselfish service and hard work delivered by the crew in Kodiak, and her supporters in Puget Sound and around the world. The KALAKALA has found a new crew that has served her faithfully. And with this tale, we count Judi Ennes as part of the KALAKALA crew too.

I first met Judi on a tough and discouraging day in the fall of 1999. We sat, and she read to me this story. I was spell bound. I thanked her for her tale, because on that tough day, her story was just what I needed to hear.

Judi wrote, 'the KALAKALA was magic, and Seattle needed her.' And Judi's story is magic, and we need to hear it, too.

Thank you, Judi..

Pete Bevis

Fog blanketed Gibson Cove. The sun rose slowly, its rays prodding through the mist to reveal the dark outlines of fishing boats, a small tugboat named Ruby, and other watercraft in various stages of disrepair tied to the crooked fingers of piers near the town of Kodiak, Alaska.

A hodge-podge of squat, shabby, fish cannery buildings lined the edge of land overlooking the quiet bay. Surrounded by hills of crab pots and rusty statues of broken cannery machinery, another shape rose, looking as if it did not belong in this desolate landscape. The mountainous hulk was decorated with a line of darkened portholes strung along its side. Splotches of rust wounds shadowed the hull. Arched windows of broken glass adorned the upper level. This smooth, mounded shape stood in contrast against the sharp lines of buildings, piled rock fills and craggy mountains. It was Kalakala, a ferryboat with a dream.

That morning, as the tide rose, Kalakala tried to shift her weight one more time to escape the lumps and bumps of the gravel and rock fill that had held her captive for over twenty years. If only, Kalakala thought, she could just stretch her stack a little or dislodge that boulder that was under her stern. Instead, she had to be satisfied with the swelling and contracting of her steel skin as determined by the temperatures of this far northern town.

Kalakala shivered, realizing another winter was not far away. Then, she looked up, as she heard her name, sung by the v-shaped formation of geese as they flew over her bow toward the south. "Kalakala (Ka lock a la), Kalakala". The native Chinook name for 'flying bird', fit her well, she admitted. The scarred ferry longed for the freedom to follow the graceful birds south and home, to Washington. The sparkling water she could see just outside the cove, teasingly invited her to wistfully dream of the days when she had skimmed the waters of Puget Sound.

Kalakala looked at the piers and saw her friend, Ruby. She called the tug, "Lil, Ruby," because she was so small. They spoke together sometimes. Kalakala talked of ferrying people and cars across the inland passages of Washington, and they discussed familiar places in Puget Sound. Ruby had been built near the place that Kalakala considered her birthplace. The little tugboat recalled how important she had felt as she pushed big ships that towered over her into the harbors of Alaska, helping them to dock safely. After so many years, they both longed for the glorious past.

Kalakala sat, unable to move from the spot where bulldozers had imprisoned her with rock and mud. Ruby was resigned to her position on a broken pier.

Kalakala's dreams of once again plying the warmer waters near Seattle had begun to fade into memory. She had been still so many years. Ferns waved from the cracks and crevices in her decks, and moss carpeted the walls and floors. Gulls squawked loudly as they glided in for a landing on her stained and dented roof.

Kalakala felt hopeless, sitting fast in a surrounding that imprisoned her and still seemed foreign after all the years. In fact, she couldn't remember exactly how long it had been since she had left Seattle, believing she was heading to a new adventure.

However, instead of exciting routes, her new owners had placed her here, in Gibson Cove, Alaska, to house a shellfish processing plant. At first, her new job was interesting. There were many busy people moving about on her decks, talking loudly above the din of the peeling and cooking of shrimp and the cracking of the long-legged crabs. Then, after feeling the crush of stone and sand pushed against her hull to keep her in place against the tides, Kalakala realized that she might never move again.

10

The once-sleek ferry was embarrassed as she looked at her reflection in the dirty water that was becoming one huge mud puddle just off her bow. Her once-shiny silver paint had turned dull gray and was streaked with red blotches of rust. Her fittings were corroded. The large, smooth doors that had enclosed the rear car deck when she ran on the open water, were stacked against a wall and marred with deep scratches. Only the graceful wrought-iron railings, tarnished brass handrails, and huge engines were reminders of her once-proud sailings across Elliot Bay to Seattle.

Kalakala dreamt often of the days when she had ferried passengers between Seattle and Bremerton. At night, her job had been to cruise around Elliot Bay while a band played music and the passengers danced. She especially enjoyed the memory of the children as they came aboard with their parents or teachers to ride the ferry and exclaim in delight at the sights. She smiled when she remembered their nickname for her, the Silver Slug, although she secretly thought she was much more beautiful than that and certainly moved faster, too.

Kalakala shivered. Despite the rays of sunshine peeking through the lifting fog, the breeze was cold. She could still see bits and pieces of crab and shrimp shells embedded in the cracks of the cement that now covered her steel decks. Anyone coming close would get a whiff of the fishy smell and stagnant water left in her bilge. She could not imagine her engine ever running strong again.

Kalakala was saddened by her condition. Even if the cannery were still running, she thought, she would feel better. She could at least feel useful. People would bring their noisy cheerfulness on board as they worked. Now, however, the cold loneliness made her feel useless and ugly. Only the eagles that circled above her and dove into the icy water to catch their salmon seemed to respect the proud ship she had once been. They would often light on the wheelhouse, lending their regal beauty like a crown atop the aged ferry. Kalakala watched the four pairs of eagles dancing in the sky above her bow, wings outstretched, talons curled, the sun reflecting the dazzling white of their heads and the shimmering black of their wings. The pairs met, touched briefly, and then soared to the pointed treetops and their nests.

One day, as she sat musing over her past, Kalakala felt someone clambering up to her deck from the wide board that served as a ramp from the ground below. He was a large, bearded man in an old sweatshirt and dark, loose pants, covered by a yellow rain slicker. There was a cap on his head and old scruffy boots on his feet. The man looked around slowly. His blue eyes widened and his head nodded thoughtfully as he recognized Kalakala's name painted above the doorway. He looked around at the rust and dirt. He spied the ferns hanging from her roof. He stepped over the forgotten garbage dropped long ago. He strode across the deck from port to starboard, dodging the crude walls that had been installed as offices. He looked over the sides and examined her hull.

Kalakala knew that he must have smelled the stink that seemed to lurk in every cranny of her hull. But, he continued, using his flashlight as he explored Kalakala from stern to bow. He examined the vast engine room. He noticed her graceful curves. He stood silent a long time, squinting out over the waters of the cove.

Finally, he inspected it all again. He crawled below to the car deck, the engine room, up the stairs, in the old freezer, and to the pilot house. He kicked the rust spots, dug into the floor, and ducked great sheets of paint hanging from the ceiling. He moved quickly now, excited at what he saw.

The burly man climbed partially through a porthole and sat on its rim, looking out at the cove. Then, in a loud voice that no one was listening to except Kalakala, he spoke. "I can feel your magic, lady." His voice changed to a whisper that only Kalakala could hear. "I'm taking you home! Seattle needs you back."

He remembers? He remembers! The ferry could hardly believe what she heard. Then she watched as he overturned an empty bucket, sat down, and pulled a pen and a checkbook from an inside pocket. Kalakala saw the check he wrote to the city of Kodiak for $1,000. Down in the corner he noted, "for the Kalakala." The ferry had lots of questions, but the man climbed back over the side and left before any of them could be answered. She watched him drive off in an old truck in the direction of Kodiak.

Watch for him, Ruby, she pleaded. Indeed, Ruby watched the bearded man arrive and park outside the small building that served as Kodiak's city hall. She also saw the same man leaving a few minutes later, his head down, the check still in his hand. He headed for a dinghy tied up near the little tug. He shook his head as he climbed into it. Then, he ripped the paper up into little pieces. He pushed the oars roughly into place and lashed at the water with them as he rowed toward a fishing boat anchored out in the bay. Ruby gently told Kalakala what had happened.

Now what? Kalakala was disappointed. The man had left. Again, she stood alone, an aged, graying hulk surrounded by cannery relics, mud, and stone. She really couldn't blame the man for giving up so quickly. She knew she shouldn't have believed the man's words, yet that's exactly what she wanted to do.

That night, she dreamt of swing music and people dancing to the rhythm on her deck as they had done on the night cruises around Elliot Bay. If she was very still, she could hear the laughter of passengers and the rustle of taffeta skirts as happy couples danced to the tunes of the Flying Bird Orchestra. She felt the steps of the 2000 children she had picked up in Bremerton on her first working voyage. She pictured the sailors dozing as she delivered them, to the naval base early in the morning. She remembered the welcoming banners she had proudly displayed during the World's Fair in 1962. She had been so faithful, gliding back and forth between the towns of Puget Sound, allowing passengers to admire the gorgeous scenery as they went about their travels. Surely this man who had just stood on her deck, remembered her unselfish service.

However, the man did not return the next day or the day after that. Kalakala knew his visit and words had not been her imagination, but she wondered how much longer she needed to be patient. Maybe . . . maybe, he would never come back.

Thus, she suffered her indignities for another cold day, then another night, then a week. Each morning, Kalakala noticed that the snow had moved another 100 feet down the mountains. She shivered in the wind and rain. Finally, it began to snow. Ice, three feet thick, filled the cove. She waited through another winter. Spring came slowly. Six more winters came and went.

Kalakala had quit dreaming by then. She only sat there, wondering when she would finish the process of rusting apart. Lil, Ruby still sat at the broken pier. They never talked like they used to. The days were endless.

Then, unbelievably, and without announcement, one sunny day, the bearded man returned. Once again, he climbed aboard. He planted his feet on the deck, cocked his head, and looked her over once again, perhaps seeing her as she used to be. He was dressed just about the same, but he placed a dufflebag at his feet and helped a small dog climb on board. Kalakala heard the man call the animal Loosie. The little brown-and-white dog followed him everywhere, her toenails tickling Kalakala and her cold wet nose investigating every inch of the rough cement deck. The ferry let herself feel just a glimmer of the past hope.

At first, Kalakala thought that the man, who called himself Peter, would just start up the engines and then they would go. But after he moved on board and placed a cot, a small cook stove, a lamp, and a radio into the old freezer, she realized that things were not going to be as easy as she had hoped.

Peter began to scrape the rust spots first. He filled a bucket with the red, crumbling metal. Loosie stayed by his side usually, or sniffed, exploring the quiet corners. People started to visit the old ferry, curious, but offering little encouragement.

"It belongs to the city," stated the mayor of Kodiak. *Peter kept scraping.*

"You couldn't buy it before, you can't buy it now!" said the city treasurer. *Peter shoveled the garbage.*

"It'll never float!" argued a fisherman. *Peter started welding.*

"She'll have to be dug out," warned a friend. *Peter looked at bulldozers.*

"You need a high tide to get her loose," decided the townspeople. *Peter read the tide tables and began to schedule.*

"You need money," demanded others. *Peter wrote to Seattle.*

"You have to have a tugboat!" declared the Coast Guard.

Peter talked to his friends. He wrote letters. He called his family. Kalakala's heart sank. She knew he didn't have much money. She believed he would become discouraged. Yet he kept writing by lamplight and talking on the phone. In the late hours, he read a thick book called Laws of the Sea.

Newspaper reporters came to visit. They shook their heads and grinned at his idea. But they took his picture, and Loosie's too, standing on the deck of Kalakala. After they left, Peter kept scraping the rust and hauling it off the ferry, two buckets at a time, one in each hand.

Then slowly, one by one, Peter's friends came to help. They stayed during their vacations or when they didn't have other work. Peter would stand on Kalakala's deck with his feet braced wide apart. "We're taking her home!" He sounded convincing. "Can't you feel the magic? Seattle needs her." Sometimes he would yell about his love for her, scaring the gulls from their perches and making Loosie bark.

People all around the world laughed. But his friends just nodded. "We'll do it one bucket at a time."

Peter argued. "No, we'll do it *two* buckets at a time."

Kalakala believed now. She could feel herself sit a little straighter. She ignored the scratches and dents. She hardly noticed the old cannery smells any more. She hoped Peter knew how excited she was.

Another year went by. Peter continued to direct his friends, as they came and went, to pound out the dents, to grind the rust, to jack-hammer the cement floor, to clear the decks, to pump out the bilge, to weld the bulkheads, and to dig out Kalakala's hull.

More time passed. However, Kalakala was determined not to be discouraged. Peter never seemed to give up. When people began to laugh again, he glared at them as he squinted out one eye and proclaimed, "We're taking her back!"

Then the officials came once more. The mayor said, "No title!"   The commissioner said, "No insurance!"

The Coast Guard said, "No permission to get underway!"

Peter held up his thick book and yelled his answer, "We'll salvage* her!"

Then he climbed off the boat and drove to town. When he came back, he had a small paper bag. He pulled out an eye patch and put it on. He looked like a pirate. He gave one to each of his helpers and one to Loosie too. "Call me Pete, Pete, the Pirate!" he demanded. Then the men circled around the flagpole and hoisted a Jolly Roger flag. He pulled on his orange vest, "a color of authority!" he stated. Peter continued to direct, yell, and encourage. He knew what had to happen.

*That means that if Peter could get the Kalakala out on the water and keep her afloat, he could claim the boat as his own.

24

So, during the day, the men pumped, cleaned, ground, painted, hammered, welded, dug, and dredged. Loosie helped by announcing visitors and chasing off the noisy seagulls. The small dog stood on the roof of the wheelhouse surveying the surrounding desolate land, ready to argue with any strangers that might come along to interrupt the important work that was going on.

Then there were the long chilly nights. One of Peter's friends, an artist, drew beautiful chalk pictures of mountains, using a rusty bulkhead that he had welded during the day, as his canvas. The rest of the men sat around the stove, telling tales and singing songs. Sometimes, they played cards or read by the dim light. Peter stared up at the ceiling, planning, as he stroked an orange and black cat, Rat's Nightmare, who had recently taken up residence aboard the ferry. The cat curled up close to the fire, cobwebs still hanging from her whiskers, satisfied and tired from doing her job in the tight, dark places.

But, morning always came again. And when the same officials with the same arguments kept coming, Peter just planted his feet on the deck, wore his eye patch, and waited for the high tide. It took a long time, but slowly Kalakala was ready.

26

T hen, the momentous day came. Everyone could feel the excitement! The mayor, the fishermen, the cannery workers, Peter's friends, and Seattle, all anticipated the high tide very early the next morning.

Stars were still sprinkled in the early morning sky. Crabs scurried to hide in Kalakala's shadows, and starfish clung to her side. Schools of small fish swam around her, kissing her silver side with open mouths.

Then it began. The tide started to lift her. She heard the sounds of the sand grinding against her hull. She felt the water swirling around her bow. She tried to think of some way to help pull her bottom off the bed of Gibson Cove.

Kalakala looked toward Kodiak. She saw the docks next to Ruby filled with people. Ruby's big brother, the Kodiak King, attached a line to her bow. Peter and his friends stood on her deck and hung on to the rail. Loosie barked her excitement and Rat's Nightmare peered from a dark doorway, cobwebs coating her whiskers.

With a strong surge of power, Kalakala finally was pulled free from the imprisoning sand and gravel. She floated. She skimmed the top of the frothy bay. The men hugged each other in their joy. The watching crowd screamed and shouted their hoorays. Lil' Ruby pulled on her lines near the pier. Even Peter may have had just one shining tear in his eye.

Kalakala was towed to Women's Bay to await another tug, the Neptune, and permission from the Coast Guard to depart. As the sun came up, the overjoyed ferry saw the eagles dance once again over her bow. She knew she was going home!

Finally, Neptune began to tow her hundreds of miles south along the coast of Alaska.

When the storms arrived, Kalakala tucked in on the lee side of the small islands to wait for calmer weather. Then, she almost flew like the South bound geese who sang her name, past British Columbia and into the inland waters of Washington.

Kalakala entered Elliot Bay once more, greeted by fireboats announcing her arrival with cascading showers from their hoses. Bag pipers, piped their welcome. Horns honked. Music played, and people danced on the pier. Seattle waved, and Peter waved back. Yes, he had been right. The Kalakala was magic and Seattle needed her. She was finally back home with joy in her heart and many dreams to come true, one-no, two-buckets at a time.

From the Author

This book is a love story between a ferry and the people who remember; between a ferry and the people who appreciate her romance of architecture and style. I found it very easy to write. Peter's determination against the odds to bring the Kalakala home, inspired the story. Yet it was my memories of growing up in the Seattle area, and enjoying rides on the Kalakala that made her point of view real to me. I find that when I board her now to speak to the volunteers or Peter, I still find the same loving determination that this story is about. Even in Seattle, her home, there is still not a clear solution for Kalakala's life. However, perseverance continues to reign. The memories that people have of traveling on the "Flying Bird" are incredible. Anyone who tours her now, and listens to her tale cannot escape noting the relationship people had with her.

My own faulty memory focuses on a ferry ride from Bremerton to Coleman docks in Seattle. Kalakala crashed, slightly damaging the pier. My brother climbed out a porthole, caught a bus home, and let my mom know that my father and I would be late for dinner. But to me, the delay did not matter, I was so impressed with her sleek, graceful bearing, even at my young age, that I enjoyed every moment spent on board.

While writing this book, I was privileged to speak with many people who remembered the Kalakala. I particularly enjoyed chatting with a gentleman who had ridden her back and forth to Bremerton as a sailor, perhaps dozing most of the way. As I shared this book with my friend that I had know for thirty years, she told me of her brother who had worked on the ferry as a deck hand and had many stories to tell. During the holidays, I browsed through a deteriorating album in an old house my husband and I acquired. Looking through the fragile post cards and photos, I delightfully discovered four small, 1"x2" photos of the Kalakala, one with Seattle in the background. I believe that thousands of these people and memory connections exist because just maybe, the Kalakala **was** "magical."

When I walk on the Kalakala now, there is such a sense of history and beauty. As a marble floor is uncovered, a rail polished, or machinery oiled, the magic returns. I can 'see' the palm room with its turtle shell ceiling, the grand staircase, the horseshoe bar, the innovative brass fire system, and women's salon, Each gutted room fills with the glory of its past when visited by those who remember, or those who wish they could.

I began this story in my classroom as a writing exercise, the year Peter brought Kalakala back to Seattle. The following summer, the few paragraphs I had started, prompted me to finish. As I continued to write the tale, I knew that it was also Peter's story. I called to ask permission to write about it. Graciously, he agreed. Then, after meeting this dynamic, artistic and determined pirate, I realized also, that Kalakala's story was beyond my limited vision. I can only continue to encourage all who read this story to become enticed as I was, to be involved in the unfinished tale of Kalakala.

Judith A. Ennes

Seattle's Famous Harbor

"Kalakala" - World Famous Streamline Ferry

KALAKALA FACTS

▲ Length: 276 ft.

▲ Beam: 55 ft., 8 in.

▲ Depth: 21 ft., 6 in.

▲ Capacity: 2000 passengers, 100 automobiles

▲ The original vessel, the Peralta is purchased by the Puget Sound Navigation Co. from Key System, near San Francisco.

▲ Capt. Alexander Peabody planned for a modernized, streamlined ferry. Boeing engineers help design her.

▲ Major restoration work is completed at Lake Washington Shipyard. Finishing touches are done at Todd Shipyard.

▲ Maiden voyage: July 3, 1935, with a speed of 17.3 knots

▲ Primary route: Seattle to Bremerton

▲ Retired: October 2, 1967

▲ In the late 1930s, runs are increased to accommodate defense workers commuting to Puget Sound Naval Shipyard.

▲ 1945: Kalakala starts weekend excursion cruises between Seattle and Victoria, B.C.; Ruby built in Everett.

▲ June 1955: Kalakala is assigned to the Port Angeles-Victoria run.

▲ 1960: The Kalakala returns to the Seattle-Bremerton run.

▲ 1962: The Kalakala is festooned with banners promoting the Seattle World's Fair

▲ October 2, 1967: The Kalakala completes her final run as a Washington State Ferry.

▲ October 3, 1967: The ferry is bought by American Freezerships to be converted into a crab-processing vessel in Dutch Harbor, Alaska.

▲ 1969: The Kalakala is purchased by Wr Grace Co. and moved to Ouzinkie, Alaska, where she processed crab.

▲ 1970: The Kalakala is moved to Gibson Cove and converted to process shrimp. Bulldozers backfilled around her with tons of rock to make it easier for shrimp boats to unload.

▲ Nov.6, 1998: The Kalakala returns home to Seattle.

▲ August 1999: The tug, Ruby XIV, donated to the Kalakala Foundation, joined Kalakala at home in Puget Sound.